The King

and other stories

Oscar Wilde

Simplified by D K Swan
and Michael West

Illustrated by Gwen Tourret

Longman

Longman Group UK Limited,
Longman House, Burnt Mill, Harlow,
Essex CM20 2JE, England
and Associated Companies throughout the world.

This simplified edition © Longman Group UK Limited 1988

First published 1988

ISBN 0-582-54158-1

Set in 10/13 point Linotron 202 Versailles
Produced by Longman Group (FE) Limited
Printed in Hong Kong

Acknowledgements

The cover background is a wallpaper design called NUAGE,
courtesy of Osborne and Little plc.

Stage 3: 1300 word vocabulary

Please look under *New words* at the back of this book
for explanations of words outside this stage.

Contents

Introduction

Oscar Wilde

Oscar Wilde was born in Dublin, Ireland, in 1854. He studied the classics (Greek and Latin languages and literature) at Trinity College, Dublin, and then at Oxford University. At both universities he was an unusually good student, and at Oxford he won a special prize for poetry.

He became a leader of the aesthetic movement. The aims of this movement were not entirely clear. Writers and artists of several kinds joined it. They shared a feeling that the industrial world – the world of factories, business, and the pursuit of riches – had lost a sense of the value of beauty. They wanted to see a return to a love of art for the sake of art, not for its value in money or social importance. Some of them looked to poetry, some to religious form, others to different kinds of art, hoping that these would bring back the spiritual side of European culture.

Writers like Oscar Wilde aimed to make their use of language – not just what they said, but how they said it – effective. You will see, in this book, some of the ways Wilde tried to put art into the telling even of his fairy stories. Notice particularly the way he uses words to put into our imaginations clear pictures which give us feelings of different kinds.

We feel pity – a sense of sorrow for other people's suffering – in a number of the stories. In one story, we feel pity for the unhappy *Happy Prince* and the little swallow, and pity for the people *they* pity.

Perhaps in that story we even pity the unfeeling head man of the city. But that is really another matter: Wilde doesn't hate the unfeeling people who filled his world, but he sees them clearly, and we see them: the lords and officers in the palace of the *young king*; Don Pedro in the story of the *Infanta*; the merchants who laughed at the *fisherman*, and others.

We share Wilde's dislike of the way the richer people of his time made appearances so important. Appearances like the right clothes:

"Won't they know me as a king if I don't have the clothing of a king?" (*The Young King*)

or the proper behaviour:

The Camarera, who was at her side, told her that a princess must not laugh so loud. (*The Birthday of the Infanta*)

or usefulness:

"Love ... is quite useless. In these difficult times we must learn useful things." (*The Nightingale and the Rose*)

or tidiness:

"We must make an order that birds must not be allowed to die here." (*The Happy Prince*)

Oscar Wilde became known as the writer of very clever plays for the theatre. The people in his plays spoke and behaved like real people. The plays seemed amusing and light, but thinking people found in them a great deal of serious feeling and an attack on an unfeeling society with false values and an insincere respect for appearances, which he called hypocrisy.

People quoted lines from Oscar Wilde's plays, and they remembered the sharp and clever things he said about famous people in conversation.

Wilde had enemies, of course. No man who says cutting things can expect to be liked by everyone. People quoted him, but many of them disliked him. One man in particular hated him: the Marquis of Queensbury. And one result of that was that Wilde spent two years of great suffering in prison. There he wrote *The Ballad of Reading Gaol*. Here are a few lines from it:

> I know not whether Laws be right,
> Or whether Laws be wrong;
> All that we know who lie in gaol
> Is that the wall is strong;
> And that each day is like a year,
> A year whose days are long.

Fairy Tales

Wilde's book of fairy tales, *The Happy Prince*, came out in 1881. A fairy tale was once "a story about fairies and other small magical people". Today we often mean a story for children with some magic in it when we call something a fairy tale.

There is certainly magic, or something like magic, in the stories of this book. In *The Young King* there is the effect of the sunlight in the church. *The Fisherman and his Soul* is very magical, with a mermaid, witches, and a palace at the bottom of the sea. *The Star Child* and *The Selfish Giant* are full of magic too. But *The Happy Prince* is almost possible, and so is *The Nightingale and the Rose*. The only story without magic is *The Birthday of the Infanta*, but that seems to work magic in us – the magic that produces pity and understanding. Like all the rest, that story works at two levels: it is a simple story for children, and, for grown-ups, a far from simple examination of the state of the world and the nature of the men and women in it.

The Young King

The young king was sitting alone in his beautiful room in the palace. He was only sixteen years old; he was wild-eyed like some animal of the forest. The servants of the old king had found him in the forest. He was sitting there playing his pipe and watching the forester's goats. This poor forester had brought him up ever since he was a baby, and the boy believed that he was his son; but he was the child of the old king's daughter.

The king's daughter had married a common man, a man far below her. He was a painter, painting pictures on the walls of the great church in which kings were crowned. But one day he went away from the princess, leaving his pictures unfinished. When the baby was only a week old he was taken away from his mother's side while she slept. The forester and his wife had no children, and lived more than a mile away in the forest. The baby was put in their hands.

The princess died.

When the old king was dying he said, "My heart is heavy because of the great wrong that I have done. Do not let the crown pass away from my family. Send for my daughter's child who is with the forester. He shall be king after me."

When the boy was brought to the palace, he showed a strange love for all beautiful things. He gave a cry of pleasure when he saw the beautiful clothes and rich jewels

1

The young king sees the beautiful clothes and jewels

which had been prepared for him. With joy he threw aside the old coat that he had worn in the forest. Whenever he could escape from the long meetings with the great lords and captains, he wandered from room to room through the palace finding beauty everywhere.

A rich merchant who had come to see the king found him kneeling in front of a beautiful picture that had just been brought from Venice. On another day, after people had searched for several hours, they found him in a little room at the north end of the palace looking with wonder at the shape of the Greek god Adonis cut in a jewel.

As he lay in his bed he was thinking of the wonderful coat of gold thread which he would wear when he was crowned, and of his jewelled crown and sceptre. The best artists in the world had planned them, and the workers were ordered to work day and night to finish them. He could see himself standing in the great church dressed as a king, wearing these wonderful things.

His eyes closed, and sleep came over him; and as he slept, he dreamed.

He dreamed that he was standing in a long, low room. All round him he heard the noise of weavers at their work of making cloth. Only a little daylight came in through narrow barred windows. Their faces were white and thin. Little children were working with them; they were weak from hunger and their little hands shook.

The young king went to one of the weavers and stood by him and watched. The weaver looked at him angrily.

"Why are you watching me?" he said. "Were you sent by our master to keep watch on us?"

"Who is your master?" asked the young king.

"Our master is a man like myself. There are only two

3

differences between us: he wears fine clothes; and, while I am weak from hunger, he suffers from having too much food."

"The land is free," said the young king, "and you are no man's slave: you are not an unpaid worker owned by a master."

"In war," answered the weaver, "the strong make slaves of the weak, and in peace the rich make slaves of the poor. We must work to live, but they pay us so little that we die. We grow the corn, but we have no bread. We are slaves, though all men call us free. But what do these things matter to you? You are not one of us: your face is too happy."

He turned away and went on weaving, and the young king saw that the thread was of gold and the cloth was cloth-of-gold. Cold fear seized his heart.

"Who are you weaving that for?" he asked.

"I am weaving it for the crowning of the young king. But what does that matter to you?"

The young king gave a loud cry and woke. He was in his own room in the palace, and through the window he saw the golden moon hanging in the sky.

He fell asleep again and dreamed. He dreamed that he was on a ship which was being rowed by hundreds of slaves. The master of the ship was sitting in front. His coat was of red silk and great silver rings pulled down his ears. The slaves had only a cloth round their middle. Each man was chained to the man next to him. The hot sun beat down upon them and a man ran up and down between them and struck them so that the blood came, to make them row faster.

At last they came to a little bay. They stopped. The

seamen seized one of the youngest slaves. They took off his chains. They tied a stone to his feet and let him down by a rope over the side of the ship. After some time he was pulled up out of the water: he had a pearl in his right hand. The seamen took it from him, then pushed him back into the water.

The young slave came up again and again; each time he brought with him a beautiful pearl. The master of the ship put the pearls in a green bag.

Then the slave came up for the last time. The pearl that he brought was the best of all. It was shaped like the full moon and brighter than the morning star. But the face of the slave was strangely white, and, as he fell down, blood came from his ears and mouth.

"Dead?" said the master. "Throw the body into the sea." He looked at the pearl: "This shall be for the sceptre of the young king."

When the young king heard this, he gave a great cry and woke. Through the window he saw the stars beginning to grow dim and the daylight coming.

He fell asleep again and dreamed. He dreamed that he was wandering through a dark forest full of strange fruit and beautiful flowers. He went on and on until he came out of the forest and there he saw a great crowd of men working in a dried-up river. They dug great holes in the ground and broke the rocks with axes. They hurried about calling to each other.

He turned and saw an old man standing behind him, holding a mirror in his hand.

"Who are these men?" he asked.

"The people in the walled cities have no food, and the wells in the country are dry," said the old man. "But these men are working in the dried-up river to find——"

"What are they trying to find?"

"Jewels – for a king's crown," said the old man.

"For what king?"

"Look in the glass and you will see him."

He looked in the glass and saw his own face.

He gave a great cry and woke. Bright sunlight was shining into the room and birds were singing in the trees of the garden.

The lords and high officers of the government came into the young king's room and bowed to him. The servants brought the coat made of cloth-of-gold and set down the crown and sceptre before him.

The young king looked at the things and saw that they were beautiful, more beautiful than anything he had ever seen. But he remembered his dreams, and he said, "Take these things away. I will not wear them."

The lords and high officers of the government were very surprised. Some of them thought that he had said this in fun, and they laughed.

He spoke to them again: "Take these things away and hide them from me. I will not wear them. This cloth was woven by the white hands of pain. There is blood in jewels and death in the heart of the pearl." And he told them his three dreams.

When the lords and officers heard this they said, "He does not know what he is saying: he is out of his mind, for a dream is only a dream. Dreams are not real things and one should take no notice of them. What do the lives of those who work for us matter? Must a man not eat until he has seen the man who grew the corn? How are the people to know that you are king if you are not dressed as a king?"

The young king looked at him. "Is that so?" he asked. "Won't they know me as a king if I don't have the clothing of a king?"

"They will not know you," said the chief officer.

"I had thought," he answered, "that there were men who looked like kings. Perhaps you are right. But I will not wear this coat and I will not be crowned with this crown. I will go out from the palace just as I came into it. Go, all of you. Let only this boy-servant remain."

He opened a big box and took out of it the rough coat which he wore when he was watching goats on the hillside: in his hand he took the stick that he carried as a goat-herd.

The boy-servant said, "Sir, I see your coat and your sceptre, but where is your crown?"

The young king took a branch of a wild-rose which had grown up near the window. He made it into a circle and put it on his head.

"This shall be my crown," he said, and he went out of his room into the Great Hall, where the lords and high officers were waiting for him. He went down into the courtyard. He got up on his horse and rode out through the great gates of the palace to go to the church to be crowned; and the boy ran beside him.

The people in the streets laughed. "It is the king's fool who is riding by," they said. He stopped and answered, "No. I am the king" – and he told them his three dreams.

A man came out of the crowd and spoke angrily to him: "The life of the poor comes from the fine things that the rich use. The making of these things gives us bread. Go back to your palace and put on the clothing of a king. Why should you care for us and what we suffer?"

"Are not the rich and the poor brothers?" asked the

young king. His eyes filled with tears and he rode on through the angry cries of the people. The boy-servant became afraid and left him.

The soldiers tried to stop him at the great gate of the church. "No one may enter here except the king," they said to him.

"I am the king," he answered angrily, and he pushed them aside.

The highest priest in the church was waiting to crown the new king. The High Priest saw the young king coming dressed as a goat-herd. He went to meet him and said, "My son, is this the dress of a king? With what crown shall I crown you? What sceptre shall I put in your hand? This should be a day of joy."

"Shall joy wear what sadness and pain have made?" said the king; and he told him his dreams.

"I am an old man," answered the High Priest, "and I know that many wrong things are done in the world; but God has made us as we are, and He is wiser than you. The weight of this world's suffering is too great for one man to bear, too heavy for one man to suffer."

"Do you say that in this house of God!" said the young king. He walked past the High Priest and knelt and bowed his head in prayer.

Suddenly a great noise came from the street outside. The lords entered, shouting, "Where is this dreamer of dreams? Where is the king who is dressed as a goat-herd? He is not fit to rule over us!"

The young king stood up. He turned and looked at them sadly.

Then sunlight poured down through the coloured glass of the window and made for him a covering far more beautiful than the coat of cloth-of-gold. The stick put out white flowers more beautiful than any pearl, and the wild rose on his head shone brighter than any jewel.

He stood there dressed as a king and the light of heaven filled the place. There was music and singing. The people fell on their knees.

The High Priest laid his hands on the young king's head. "A greater One than I has crowned you," he said, and knelt down before him.

The Birthday of the Infanta

It was the birthday of the Infanta, the daughter of the King of Spain. She was just twelve years old, and the sun was shining brightly on the garden of the palace. The little princess was playing with her friends in the garden. From a window in the palace the sad king watched her. He was sadder than usual today because, as he looked at the Infanta, he saw how like her mother she was. He thought of the young queen her mother, who had come from France. She died soon after her child was born, before she had ever seen the beautiful flowers in the garden or eaten the fruit from the fruit trees which grew round the courtyard.

He had loved her so much that he could not let the grave hide her from him. An Egyptian doctor had made her body remain fresh as it was in life, and it lay in the small church of the palace just as it had been put there on that windy March day nearly twelve years ago. Once every month the king went there and knelt by her side calling out, "My queen! My queen!"

Today the king seemed to see his queen again just as he had seen her first in the palace of the King of France when he was fifteen years old, and she was not much older than the Infanta today. They were promised to each other in marriage, and, later, they were married and she came to Spain. His whole married life seemed to come back to him today as he watched the Infanta playing in the garden. She had the same pretty manner as the queen, the same way of moving her head as she talked, the same proud beautiful mouth, the same wonderful smile as she looked up at the window or held out her little hand for some Spanish gentleman to kiss. But the king felt too sad to enjoy the laughter of the children or to look at the bright sunlit garden. He hid his face in his hands, and, when the Infanta looked up again at the window, the king had gone.

"Well," she said, "he might have stayed with me on my birthday! Why has he gone away? Has he gone to deal with questions of government? What do they matter today? I think he has gone to that dark little church – the church I am never allowed to enter. How silly of him when the sun is shining so brightly and everyone is so happy!"

She walked to the big tent in which her birthday show was to be given. Her uncle, Don Pedro, and the Camarera, a grand lady who attended the Infanta, went with her. Some boys, riding wooden horses, pretended to fight a battle. Then there was a man walking along a rope. An Indian brought a basket covered with a cloth. He put it down and played music on a pipe: then snakes came out of the basket and moved their heads to the music. Then he put a seed in the sand and covered it with a cloth, and a tree grew up out of it. He covered it again and there were flowers on the tree. He brought eggs out of his nose. Then he took one egg and changed it into a little bird, which flew away. The children were delighted with his magic.

Some schoolboys did a beautiful dance. Then some Africans, dressed in brightly coloured clothes, came and sat in a ring and played music. And then another man led in a bear and it stood up on its back legs and danced, and did all sorts of funny things.

The funniest thing of all was the dancing of the little dwarf. He had very short legs and a very big head. He was so ugly that the children gave a shout of delight and the Infanta laughed so much that the Camarera, who was at her side, told her that a princess must not laugh so loud.

It was the first time such a strange thing had been seen. The dwarf had been found by two Spanish lords: he was running wild in the forest. His father was glad to sell such an ugly child to the gentlemen. They took him to the palace as a surprise for the Infanta. The strangest and funniest thing about the dwarf was that he did not seem to know how curious and ugly he looked. Indeed he seemed quite happy: when the children laughed, he laughed. At the end of each dance he made a funny little bow to each of the children, smiling at them as if he were one of themselves – not a strange, badly-shaped thing made for others to laugh at.

The Infanta was delighted with him, and he could not keep his eyes off her: he seemed to dance just for her. At the end she took a white rose out of her hair and threw it across to him. He took the flower and kissed it. Then he put his hand on his heart and went down on one knee before her, smiling, and his little eyes were bright with pleasure.

The Infanta kept on laughing at this, long after the little dwarf had gone out of the tent. She asked her uncle to have the dance done again, but the Camarera said, "The sun is too hot and the Infanta should go back to the palace for her birthday dinner." So the Infanta stood up and gave orders that the little dwarf was to dance again for her in the late afternoon. She went back to the palace, and the children followed her.

The little dwarf heard that the Infanta herself wanted him to dance a second time. He was so proud that he ran out

The dwarf goes on one knee to the Infanta

into the garden, kissing the white rose and jumping up and down with delight. He told the flowers: "The Infanta has given me this beautiful white rose and has ordered me to dance for her a second time." They bowed their heads but they did not seem to hear him. He told the birds, but they went on singing; perhaps their song was about him and the Infanta.

"The Infanta has given me a white rose and she loves me. Oh, I wish I had gone back into the palace with her. I would never have left her side. I would have been her friend and played with her and taught her all kinds of delightful things. I would have made a pipe and played music on it to her. I know the voices of the birds and would teach her how to call them to her. I would tell her about the little bird that I kept when its mother was shot, and how it came and fed out of my hand. Yes! She must come to the forest and play with me. We'll dance on the fresh grass and look at all the things in the forest; and when she is tired, I'll find a soft bank of flowers where she may rest."

He looked at the palace. The doors and windows were shut to keep out the midday heat. He wandered about. Then he saw a little door which was open. He went through it and found that he was in a great hall; there was gold everywhere and the floor was made of coloured stones. But the little Infanta was not there.

At the end of the hall there was a second room. In the centre there was a big round table with red books on it. This was the room in which the high officers of the country met.

The little dwarf began to be afraid, but he thought of the pretty Infanta. "I must go on," he said, "and find her. I will find her alone and tell her that I love her. I must meet the Infanta before she goes down into the garden and ask her to come away with me when I have finished my dance. I know that she will come with me to the forest – if only I can find her." He smiled as he thought of it.

He went into the next room. This was the brightest and most beautiful of all the rooms. The tables and chairs were made of silver, and the floor was of green stone, green as the sea. But he was not alone!

He saw someone – a small person – standing in the shadow near a doorway at the other end of the room. Watching him! He gave a cry of joy, and moved out into the sunlight. As he did so, the other one moved too, and he saw it clearly. This was not the Infanta! It was the ugliest thing he had ever seen. It was not shaped like other people. It had short legs and long arms and a big head covered with long black hair. He looked angrily at it; and it looked back at him – angrily. He laughed, and it laughed, holding its hands to its sides, as his hands were held. He bowed to it, and it bowed to him. He went towards it and it came to meet him, step by step as he stepped.

"What is it?" He looked at the rest of the room. Everything was seen again in this wall of clear water – picture for picture, chair for chair, table for table.

He took the white rose and kissed it. That other one had a rose too! It kissed it and pressed it to its heart. He was looking at himself in a mirror!

When the truth came to him, he gave a cry and fell weeping to the ground. So it was he who was so ugly, so fearful to look at, with those short legs and long arms and that black hair! The children had been laughing at him. He had thought that the little Infanta loved him, but she was only laughing at his ugliness, and she wanted to see him again so as to laugh still more.

"Why didn't they leave me in the forest where there was no glass to show me how ugly I am? Why didn't my father kill me, not sell me as a show – as a thing to be wondered at and a cause for laughter?"

Hot tears poured down his face, and he pulled the white rose to pieces and threw them away. The other one did the same. When he looked at it, it looked at him with a face full of pain. He covered his eyes and lay like some wounded thing in the shadow.

Just then the Infanta with her friends came into the room. They saw the ugly little dwarf lying on the ground and beating the floor with his hands in the strangest way. They gave shouts of happy laughter and stood round him and watched him.

"His dancing was very funny," said the Infanta, "and this is even funnier."

The little dwarf did not look up. He lay there weeping – very quietly. Then he gave a strange cry and put his hand to his side. Then he fell back and lay there.

"That was wonderful!" said the Infanta. "But now you must dance for me."

"Yes," cried all the children, "you must get up and dance, because you are as good as the dancing bear, and much funnier."

But the little dwarf made no answer.

The Infanta was angry. She called her uncle, Don Pedro, who was walking with the king's doctor in the garden outside.

"My funny little dwarf won't obey me," she cried. "You must wake him up and tell him to dance for me."

Don Pedro hit the dwarf: "You must dance," he said. "The Infanta of Spain wishes to see you dance."

But the little dwarf did not move.

"I must send for a servant to give him a beating," said Don Pedro.

The king's doctor knelt beside the little dwarf and put his hand on his heart. Then he stood up.

"Oh, princess, your funny little dwarf will never dance again. That is very sad, for he is so ugly that he might have made even the king laugh."

"Why won't he dance again?" asked the Infanta.

"Because his heart is broken: he was so sad that he didn't want to live. He is dead."

The Infanta was angry. "From now on," she cried, "those who come to play with me must have no hearts." And she ran out into the garden.

The Happy Prince

The statue of the Happy Prince stood high above the city. It was covered all over with thin leaves of gold. For eyes it had two bright blue jewels, and there was a large red jewel on the top of its sword.

Everyone thought that it was very beautiful.

"Why can't you be like the Happy Prince?" mothers said to their little boys when they cried.

"I'm glad there is someone in the world who is happy," sad men said as they looked at the statue.

One night a little swallow flew over the city. All the other swallows had flown to Egypt on their long wings but he had stayed behind. He arrived at the city at night.

"Where can I stay?" he said. "I hope there is some place where I can stay tonight."

Then he saw the statue.

"I'll stay there," he said. "It's high up, with plenty of fresh air." He came down just between the feet of the Happy Prince.

"I have a golden bedroom!" he said, as he looked round and prepared to go to sleep. Just as he put his head under his wing, a large drop of water fell on him.

He looked up. "That's a very strange thing!" he said. "There isn't a cloud in the sky, and the stars are clear and bright; but it's raining!"

Then another drop fell.

"What is the use of a statue if it can't keep the rain off?" he said. "I must find some other place." And he decided to fly away. But before he had opened his wings, a third drop fell. He looked up and saw – Ah! What did he see?

The eyes of the Happy Prince were filled with tears. Tears were running down his golden face. The face was so beautiful in the moonlight that the swallow felt very sorry for him.

"Who are you?" asked the swallow.

"I am the Happy Prince."

"Then why are you weeping? You have made me quite wet with your tears."

"When I was alive," said the prince, "and had a heart like any other man, I didn't know what tears were. I never wept because I lived in a palace into which sadness was never allowed to come. In the daytime I played with my friends in the garden, and in the evening I danced in the great hall. There was a high wall round the garden, and I never asked what lay on the other side, because everything on my side was so beautiful. So I was called the Happy Prince; and I was happy – if pleasure is the same as happiness. I was pleased with the little world in which I lived. Now I am dead, and they have set me up here so high that I can see all the ugliness and unhappiness of my city. My heart now is made of lead. But even that leaden heart can feel; and I weep."

"Oh," said the swallow to himself, "he isn't all made of gold: he is only gold on the outside."

"Far away," said the Happy Prince in a low voice, "far away from here there is a poor house in a little street. One of the windows is open, and through the window I can see a woman seated at a table. Her face is very thin and she has rough, red hands. She is a needlewoman. She is making a dress for one of the queen's ladies to wear at a

The swallow sees that the Happy Prince is weeping

dance in the palace. Her little boy is lying on a bed in the corner of the room. He is very ill. He is asking for fruit. She has nothing to give him except water from the river; so he is crying. Swallow, swallow, little swallow, will you take her the red jewel from the top of my sword? My feet are fixed and I can't move."

"My friends are waiting for me in Egypt," said the swallow.

"Swallow, swallow, little swallow," said the prince. "Won't you stay with me for one night and do this for me? The boy is crying and his mother is so sad."

"I don't like boys," answered the swallow. "Last summer two boys threw stones at me when I was flying over the river."

But the Happy Prince looked so sad: the little swallow was sorry for him. "It's very cold here," he said; "but I'll stay with you for one night and do what you ask."

"Thank you, little swallow," said the prince.

So the swallow took the great red jewel from the prince's sword and flew away with it over the roofs of the town.

He passed by the church and heard the sound of singing. He passed by the palace and heard the sound of dancing. A beautiful girl came to a window with her lover. "How wonderful the stars are," he said to her; "and how wonderful is the power of love!"

"I hope my dress will be ready for the great dance next week," she said; "but the needlewomen are so lazy."

He passed over the river and over the business part of the town. At last he came to the poor little house and looked in. The boy was lying restlessly on the bed and the mother had fallen asleep: she was so tired. He flew in and put the great red jewel on the table near the woman's hand. Then he flew round the bed beating down the air on to the boy's face with his wings.

"Oh," said the boy, "my face doesn't feel so hot. I think I'm getting better." And he fell asleep.

Then the swallow flew back to the Happy Prince and told him what he had done. "It's strange," he said; "I feel quite warm now, although it's so cold."

"That is because you have done a good thing," said the prince. The little swallow fell asleep.

When day came the swallow flew down to the river and had a bath. A learned man saw him. "What a curious thing!" he said. "A swallow in winter! That is very unusual. I must make a note of it!"

"I'll go to Egypt tonight," thought the swallow, and he felt very happy as he flew over all the great buildings in the town.

When the moon rose, he flew back to the Happy Prince. "Is there anything you want me to do for you in Egypt?" he said. "I'm just starting to fly there."

"Swallow, swallow, little swallow," said the prince. "Won't you stay with me for one more night?"

"My friends are waiting for me in Egypt," answered the swallow.

"Swallow, swallow, little swallow," said the prince, "far away across the city I see a young man sitting in a little room at the top of a house. He is sitting at a table covered with papers. At his side there are some dead flowers. His hair is brown and he has large dreamy eyes. He is trying to finish the story that he is writing, but he is too cold to write any more. There is no fire in the room, and he is weak with hunger."

"I'll wait with you for one more night," said the swallow, who was really very kind. "Shall I take another red jewel to him?"

"I have no other red jewel," said the prince. "My eyes are all that I have left. They are beautiful blue stones brought from India a thousand years ago. Take one of them to him. He will sell it to the jeweller and buy wood for his fire, and food, and finish his story."

"Take out your eye, dear prince?" said the swallow. "I can't do that!" And he began to weep.

"Swallow, swallow, little swallow," said the prince, "do as I order you!"

So the swallow took out the prince's eye and flew away to the room where the young man lived at the top of the house. It was easy to get in because there was a hole in the roof. The young man was sitting with his head in his hands, so he did not hear the bird's wings. When he looked up, he found a beautiful blue jewel lying on the dead flowers.

"Someone likes my stories!" he cried. "This has come from someone who has read my books and thinks them good. Now I can finish writing my story!" He looked quite happy.

On the next day the swallow flew down to the river and watched the seamen pulling big boxes and bags out of the ships with ropes. They shouted to each other as each one came up. "I'm going to Egypt!" cried the swallow; but no one listened to him.

When the moon came up he flew back to the Happy Prince. "I have come to say goodbye to you," he said.

"Swallow, swallow, little swallow," said the prince, "won't you stay one more night with me?"

"It's winter," answered the swallow. "It's getting very

cold, and snow will come. In Egypt the sun is warm and the trees are green. Dear prince, I must leave you; but I will never forget you."

"A little girl is standing there in the square below. She is selling boxes of matches. She has let her matches fall in the water and they are all spoiled. Her father will beat her if she doesn't take some money home, and she is crying. Take out my other eye and give it to her, and her father won't beat her."

"I'll stay with you for one more night," said the swallow, "but I can't take out your other eye. You would be quite blind then: you wouldn't be able to see!"

"Swallow, swallow, little swallow," said the prince. "Do as I order you!"

So he took out the prince's other eye and flew down with it. He flew past the match girl and put the jewel in her hand.

"What a beautiful piece of glass!" cried the little girl; and she ran home laughing.

Then the swallow flew back to the prince. "You are blind now," he said, "so I'll stay with you always."

"No," said the poor prince, "you must go away to Egypt."

"I'll stay with you always," said the swallow, and he slept at the prince's feet.

All the next day he stayed with the prince, and he told him stories of what he had seen in strange lands.

"Dear little swallow," said the prince, "you tell me about strange and wonderful things, but the suffering of men and women is stranger than anything. Fly over my city, little swallow, and tell me what you see there."

So the swallow flew over the great city and saw the rich

24

eating and drinking in their beautiful houses, while the beggars were sitting at the gate. He flew into the dark lanes and saw the white faces of hungry children looking out with sad eyes at the black streets. Two little boys were lying under a bridge – lying in each other's arms to try to keep themselves warm. "How hungry we are!" they said. "You mustn't lie here," shouted the watchman, and they wandered out into the rain.

Then he flew back and told the prince what he had seen.

"I am covered with fine gold," said the prince. "You must take it off, leaf by leaf, and give it to my poor people."

The swallow pulled off leaf after leaf, till the Happy Prince looked dim and grey. He took leaf after leaf to the poor, and the children's faces became brighter and they played games in the street. "We have bread now!" they cried.

Then the snow came, and ice came after the snow. The streets looked as if they were made of silver. Ice hung down from the roofs of the houses. Everyone went about in thick coats.

The poor little swallow became colder and colder, but he would not leave the prince: he loved him too much to leave him.

At last he knew that he was going to die.

"Goodbye, dear prince!" he said. "Will you let me kiss you?"

"I'm glad that you are going to Egypt at last," said the prince. "You have stayed here too long. Kiss me, because I love you."

"I'm not going to Egypt," said the swallow. "I'm going to the House of Death."

He kissed the prince, and fell down dead at his feet.

Just then there was a curious sound inside the statue, a CRACK as if something had broken. The leaden heart had broken in two pieces.

Early next morning the head man of the city was walking below with two of his friends. He looked up at the statue. "The Happy Prince doesn't look very bright!" he said. "The red stone has fallen out of his sword; his eyes are gone, and he isn't golden now. He looks more like a beggar."

"Yes! More like a beggar than a prince," said the friends.

"Here's a dead bird at his feet!" said the head man of the city. "We must make an order that birds must not be allowed to die here."

So they pulled down the statue of the Happy Prince and they put it in the fire and melted it and a stream of bright red liquid metal ran out.

"What a strange thing!" said the workmen. "This broken piece of lead won't melt. We must throw it away." So they threw it away with the dead swallow.

God said to one of his servants, "Bring me the two best things – the things worth more than anything else – in the city." They brought to Him the leaden heart and the dead bird.

"Yes, you have brought the right things," God said. "This little bird shall sing for ever in the Garden of Heaven, and the Happy Prince shall be in my City of Gold."

The Fisherman and his Soul

The young fisherman went out in his boat every evening, and threw his nets into the water.

When the wind blew away from the land he caught nothing – or very little – and rough waves met him as he came back. But, when the wind blew to the land, the fish came in from the deep sea and went into his nets; and he took them and sold them in the town.

One evening the net was so heavy that he could hardly pull it up into the boat. He laughed and said, "Perhaps I have caught all the fish in the sea! Or perhaps I have caught some strange and fearful thing which men will want to see – and pay money to see it."

He pulled and pulled: the net came nearer and nearer to the boat. At last it came to the top of the water.

There were no fish in it. There was no strange or fearful thing, but only a mermaid lying asleep. Her hair was like gold; each hair was like a thread of gold. Her body was silver and pearl. She was so beautiful that the young fisherman was filled with wonder. He took her up in his arms. When he touched her she gave a cry of fear. She opened her eyes, which were of the deepest, deepest blue, and tried to escape; but he held her and would not let her go.

When she saw that she could not escape, she began to weep. "Please, please let me go!" she said. "I am the daughter of the King of the Sea – his only daughter. He has only me and he is very old and alone."

The young fisherman answered, "I'll let you go only if you make a promise. Promise me that, whenever I call you, you will come and sing to me. The fish love to listen to the song of the People of the Sea; so they will come into my nets and my nets will be full."

"Will you really let me go if I promise that?" cried the mermaid.

"Yes, I will let you go," said the young fisherman.

So she made the promise. He opened his arms and she went down into the water.

The young fisherman went out in his boat every evening. He called to the mermaid, and she came up out of the water and sang to him. She sang to him about the People of the Sea as they move from cave to cave carrying their young ones with them. She sang about the palace of the king with its roof of clear blue jewels and its floor of pearl. She sang about the gardens of the sea where the sea-plants wave in the water and bright sea-flowers grow on the rocks, and the fishes are like birds moving among them. And, as she sang, the big fish came in from the deep sea to listen to her, and the young fisherman threw his nets round them and caught them. When his boat was full, the mermaid went down into the sea.

The mermaid never came near him so that he could touch her. He tried to catch her, but she went down into the water and he did not see her again that day. Each day the sound of her voice became sweeter in his ears. It became so sweet that he forgot his nets and took no care of his boat. The fish went by but he took no notice of them. He sat in his boat and listened. He listened as darkness came round him and the moonlight was like silver on his brown arms.

The fisherman catches the mermaid in his net

One evening he called to her, "Little mermaid! Little mermaid, I love you. Take me for your husband, because I love you."

But the mermaid answered, "No, you have a soul – the soul of man, which God has given you. If you can send away your soul, I shall love you."

The young fisherman said, "What use is my soul to me! I can't see it. I can't touch it. Certainly I'll send it away!"

He gave a cry of joy and held out his arms: "I'll send my soul away and you shall be my wife and we'll live together in the deepest part of the sea, and you'll show me all the wonderful things that you sang about."

The little mermaid laughed with pleasure and hid her face in her hands.

"But how shall I send my soul away?" cried the fisherman. "Tell me how I can do it, and it shall be done."

"I don't know," said the little mermaid. "The People of the Sea have no souls."

She went down into the sea looking sadly at him.

Early the next morning when the sun was just rising behind the hills, the young fisherman went to the priest's house and called.

"Come in," said the priest.

"Father," said the young fisherman, "I am in love with one of the People of the Sea; but because of my soul, I can't marry her. Tell me how I can send my soul away from me, because I don't need it. What use is my soul to me? I can't see it. I can't touch it. I don't know it."

The priest answered, "Foolish man! The soul was given to us by God. There is nothing on earth which is worth more to you than your soul. It is worth all the gold and jewels of the kings. It is a fearful thing to lose your soul. As for the People of the Sea, they are lost: they have no souls. They are like beasts which do not know right from wrong. There is no life after death for them – no heaven."

"Father," said the young fisherman, "once in my net I caught the daughter of the King of the Sea. She is more beautiful than the morning star, and whiter than the moon. For her body I would give my soul, for her love I would give my hope of heaven. Tell me what I ask and let me go in peace."

"Away! Away!" cried the priest, and he drove him away from the door.

The young fisherman went into the city. When the merchants saw him coming they called to him and said, "What have you got to sell?"

"I will sell my soul. What use is it to me?"

The merchants laughed at him. "What use is it to us? It isn't worth a penny. Sell us your body to be a slave, but don't talk about your soul; it's worth nothing to us."

The young fisherman thought, "This is very strange. The priest tells me that the soul is worth all the gold in the world, but the merchants say that it isn't worth a penny." He went out of the city and came down to the seashore and began to wonder what he should do.

At midday he remembered one of his friends who had told him about a witch. He ran along the sand and came to the cave in which she lived. Her magic told her that he was coming and she laughed and let down her red hair and stood at the opening of her cave.

"What do you want?" she cried as he came running towards her. "I can give you anything you want; but everything has its price."

"I want only a little thing," said the young fisherman, "but the priest was angry when I asked him for it and drove me away. It's only a little thing that I want, but the merchants laughed at me. So I have come to you, although men say that you are bad. Whatever your price is, I will pay it."

"What do you want?" said the witch, coming nearer to him.

"I want to send my soul away from me," answered the young fisherman.

The witch hid her face. "Pretty boy, pretty boy," she said. "That is a fearful thing to do."

He laughed. "My soul is no use to me," he answered. "I can't see it. I can't touch it. I don't know it."

"What will you give me if I tell you?" asked the witch, looking down at him with her beautiful eyes.

"Five pieces of gold, and my nets, and the house that I live in and the boat that I sail. Only tell me how to lose my soul and I'll give you all that I have."

She laughed. "I'm a witch, so I can have all the gold and silver that I want. I serve One who is richer than all the kings of this world."

"What then shall I give you? What shall I do?"

She put her thin white hand on his head and she smiled at him as she spoke. "You must dance with me, pretty boy," she said.

"Only that? Nothing but that?" cried the young fisherman.

"Only that," she answered, and she smiled at him again.

"Then at sunset in some secret place we shall dance together," he said, "and, after we have danced, you will tell me the thing that I wish to know."

"No," she said. "Not at sunset, but when the moon is full. Tonight you must come to the top of the mountain. It is the witches' meeting place, and He will be there."

"Who is 'He'?" asked the young fisherman. "Who is this person of whom you speak?"

"Go tonight, and stand near the tree on the top of the mountain and wait for me. When the moon is full I will be with you and we'll dance together on the grass."

"But will you promise to tell me how I may send my soul away from me?"

She moved out into the sunlight and it shone on her red hair.

"I promise," she answered.

"You are the best of witches," cried the young fisherman, "and I'll dance with you tonight on the top of the mountain."

He took off his cap and bowed to her. Then he ran back to the town filled with joy.

The witch watched him as he went. Then she went into her cave. She looked at herself in her mirror. "He ought to have been mine!" she said. "I am as beautiful as she."

That evening when the moon had risen, the young fisherman climbed to the top of the mountain and stood under the branches of the tree. The sea lay far down below, bright in the moonlight, and the shadows of the fishing boats moved in the little bay.

At midnight the witches came flying through the air.

"Phew!" they said, as they came down to the ground. "What is this smell? We smell someone here that we do not know!"

The young witch came last of all. Her long red hair flowed out behind her. Then she came down to the ground. She wore a dress of gold and a little green cap.

"Where is he? Where is he?" cried the witches when they saw her. She laughed and ran to the tree and took the fisherman by the hand. She led him out into the moonlight and began to dance. They danced round and round, and the young witch jumped so high that he could see her red shoes.

Then there was the sound of a horse; but no horse could be seen. He felt afraid.

"Faster! Faster!" cried the witch. She put her arms round his neck. Someone, some fearful thing was watching him. Then, under the shadow of the rock, he saw someone who had not been there before.

It was a man dressed in black. His face was white, but his mouth was like a red flower. His hands were white and heavy with jewelled rings. On the grass beside him there was a hat with a long feather.

The young fisherman watched him. At last their eyes met, and wherever he danced the eyes of the man followed him.

Suddenly the dancers stopped. They went, two by two, and kissed the man's hands. He smiled proudly, but he kept looking at the fisherman.

"Now, let us go to him," said the witch, and she led him up. He felt a strong wish to obey, and he followed her. He came close to the man. Without knowing why he did it, he called out the name of God. Then all the witches cried out and flew away. The man closed his eyes in pain. Then he went over to a group of trees and called. A horse came running to meet him. As he jumped up on to it he turned round and looked at the fisherman sadly.

The witch with the red hair tried to fly away too, but the fisherman caught her arm and held her.

"Let me go!" she cried. "You have said a name which should not be named."

"No!" he answered. "I won't let you go till you have told me the secret."

"What secret?" said the witch, fighting like a wild cat to free herself.

"You know!" he answered.

Her green eyes became dim with tears. "Ask me anything except that!"

He laughed and held her more strongly.

When she saw that she could not free herself, she said, "Surely I am as beautiful as the Daughter of the Sea," and she put her face close to his.

He pushed her away. "If you don't keep your promise I'll kill you."

Her face was grey. "All right," she said. "It is your soul, not mine. Do with it as you wish."

She took out a little knife in a case made of green snakeskin.

"What men call the shadow of the body is not the shadow of the body: it is the body of the soul. Stand on the shore with your back to the moon. Cut your shadow away from your feet and order your soul to leave you; and it will do so."

He took the knife. Then he went to the edge of the mountain and began to climb down. His soul inside him called out to him: "I have lived with you for all these years and have been your servant. Don't send me away from you now! What wrong have I done you?"

The young fisherman laughed. "You have done me no wrong, but I don't need you. Go wherever you wish, but don't trouble me. My love is calling to me."

The fisherman stood on the sand with his back to the moon. His shadow lay in front of him.

His soul said, "If you must drive me away from you, don't send me away without a heart. There is no love nor kindness in the world; give me your heart to take with me."

"What should I love my love with, if I give you my heart?" he cried.

"Give me your heart," said his soul, "for the world is very hard, and I am afraid."

"My heart is my love's," he answered. "So do not wait, but go!"

"Should I not love too?" asked his soul.

"Go! I don't need you," cried the young fisherman, and he took the little knife out of its case of snakeskin and cut away the shadow from round his feet. It rose up and stood in front of him, and looked at him – and it was just like himself.

He drew back and put away the knife. He was afraid. "Go!" he said, "and never let me see your face again!"

"No! We must meet again," said the soul. Its voice was very quiet.

"How shall we meet?" cried the young fisherman. "Will you follow me into the deepest part of the sea?"

"Once every year I'll come to this place and call to you," said the soul. "Perhaps you may need me."

"Why should I need you?" cried the young fisherman. "But do what you like."

Then he jumped into the sea, and the little mermaid rose up to meet him, and put her arms round his neck and kissed him.

The soul stood close on the shore and watched them. When they had gone down into the sea, it went away weeping.

When one year had passed the soul came down to the shore and called to the young fisherman, and he came out of the sea and said, "Why do you call to me?"

The soul answered, "Come nearer so that I may speak to you, because I have seen wonderful things."

So the fisherman came near and listened.

The soul said to him: "When I left you, I travelled to the east. From the east comes everything that is wise; from the east comes all wisdom. I came at last to a city. I wandered through its streets and came to the garden of its god. Priests moved silently among the trees. In the garden there was a rose-red house in which the god lived. One of the priests came to me and asked me, 'What is your wish?'

"I said, 'I wish to see the god.' Then he led me into the house. There was no god there; but only a mirror made of metal set on a table made of stone.

"I said to the priest. 'Where is the god?'

"He said, 'There is no god, but this mirror is the Mirror of Wisdom. It shows everything in heaven and on earth. Those who have this mirror know everything. Nothing is hidden from them.'

"I stole the mirror and I have hidden it in a place only one day's journey from here. Let me enter into you again and be your servant, and you shall be wiser than all the wise men."

The young fisherman laughed: "Love is better than wisdom," he cried, "and the little mermaid loves me." He went back into the sea; and the soul went away weeping.

After the second year, the soul came down to the shore and called to the young fisherman. The fisherman rose up out of the sea and said, "Why do you call to me?"

The soul answered, "Come nearer so that I may speak

to you, because I have seen wonderful things. When I left you, I journeyed to the south. All gold and jewels, all riches come from the south. I journeyed for many days and came to the city of Ashtar. The king of that city has a ring on his finger: it is the Ring of Riches. He who has that ring is richer than all the kings of the world. I went into the king's palace. The soldiers struck at me, but they could not hurt me. The king said, 'Who are you? Why can't we hurt you? Please leave my city tonight, because while you are here I am no longer its lord.'

"I answered, 'I will go if you will give me what I ask.'

"He said: 'I will give you half of my riches.'

"I said, 'Give me the ring that is on your finger.' "

Then the soul said to the fisherman, "I have hidden the Ring of Riches in a cave only one day's journey from here. Come with me and take it, and you will be richer than all the kings of this world."

The young fisherman laughed. "Love is better than riches," he cried, "and the little mermaid loves me." He went back into the sea; and the soul went away weeping.

At the end of the third year the soul came down to the shore and called to the fisherman, and he rose up out of the sea. The soul said, "Come nearer, so that I may speak to you, because I have seen wonderful things. On my journeys I came to a city in which there is a house near the river. Seamen come to that house to drink wine. As I sat there, an old man came in and played music, and a girl came and danced. Her face was covered so that I could not see it, but her white feet moved like little birds: they hardly seemed to touch the ground. I have never seen such beautiful feet, or such wonderful dancing. It is only a few days' journey from this place."

The young fisherman remembered that the little mermaid had no feet and could not dance, and he said, "It is only a short journey and then I can return to my love." He laughed and went up on to the shore. He held out his arms to his soul. The soul gave a great cry of joy and entered into him.

They travelled all that night and came to a city.

They went into the city. As they passed along the Street of the Jewellers the young fisherman saw a fine silver cup. The soul said to him, "Take that cup and hide it." So he took the cup and they went quickly out of the city.

After they had gone some way the young fisherman threw the cup away. He said to his soul, "Why did you tell me to take that cup? It was an evil thing to do."

But his soul answered, "It doesn't matter."

On the evening of the second day they came to another city. As they passed along the street the young fisherman saw a child standing with a pot of water; and his soul said to him, "Strike that child." So he hit the child, and it wept. Then they went quickly out of the city.

After they had gone a short way the young fisherman became angry. "Why did you tell me to strike the child? That was an evil thing to do."

But his soul answered, "It doesn't matter."

Late on the evening of the third day they came to another city. The young fisherman sat down and rested. After a time a merchant came by. He said, "Why are you sitting here in the street?"

The young fisherman said, "I don't know any place in this city where I may sleep. I haven't any friends here who would take me in."

The merchant said, "Aren't we all brothers? Didn't one God make us all? Come with me to my house."

So the young fisherman went and slept at the merchant's house.

Three hours before sunrise, while it was still dark, his soul woke him and said, "Go to the merchant's room; kill him and take his gold. We need it." There was a knife lying near the merchant and by the side of his bed there were three bags of gold. The young fisherman put out his hand and touched the knife. The merchant awoke and said, "Do you return evil for good and pay with blood for the kindness I have shown you?"

The soul said, "Strike him!" He struck him and took the bags of gold. When they had gone some distance from the city the young fisherman said, "Why did you tell me to kill the merchant and take his gold? – You are evil!"

The soul answered, "It doesn't matter."

"No!" cried the young fisherman. "It does matter. You have made me do evil things. Why have you done this to me?"

His soul answered, "When you sent me out into the world, you didn't give me a heart; so I learned to do all these things."

The young fisherman said, "You are evil! You have made me forget my love and led me into evil ways." He threw the bags of gold away. "I won't travel with you any more. As I sent you away before, so I'll send you away now!"

He turned his back to the moon, and with the little knife he tried to cut away that shadow of the body which is the soul. But the soul said, "A man may send his soul away once in his life, but a man who receives his soul back must keep it with him for ever."

The young fisherman said, "I'll go back to the little bay where the mermaid used to sing. I'll call to her and tell her of the evil that I have done."

His soul said, "The world has many women who are more beautiful than she is. There are the dancing girls of Samaris. They laugh while they dance and their laughter is as clear as the laughter of water. Don't trouble yourself any more, but come with me to that city."

The young fisherman did not answer, but journeyed back to the little bay where his loved one used to sing. When he came there he called to the little mermaid. But she did not come.

His soul said, "You aren't getting much pleasure out of your love. Come with me because I know where the Land of Pleasure is, and what things are done there."

The young fisherman did not answer. He built a hut among the rocks and he called to the mermaid every day and every night; but she never rose up out of the sea to meet him.

When a year had passed, his soul thought, "I have offered evil things, but the power of his love was too great. Now I'll offer good things and perhaps he'll come with me."

So the soul said, "I have told you of the joy of the world, but you wouldn't listen. Now I'll tell you of the world's pain. I'll tell you about those who have no food, about men dying of sickness. Let's go and help these people; let's go and help the poor, the sick, the unhappy."

But the young fisherman did not answer.

When the second year had passed the soul said, "I have offered you evil, and I have offered you good as well, but your love is stronger than I am. Let me come into your heart so that I may be one with you as I was before."

"Certainly you may enter," said the young fisherman. "When you went through the world with no heart, you must have suffered greatly."

"I can't find any way into your heart," said his soul. "There is no place where I may enter, because your heart is so full of love."

"I wish I could help you," said the young fisherman.

As he spoke, there came a great sound of weeping from the sea – the cry that men hear when one of the People of the Sea is dead. The young fisherman left his hut and ran down to the shore.

The black waves came hurrying in to the shore, bringing with them something which was white – whiter than silver. They brought it to the shore. The young fisherman saw the body of the little mermaid lying at his feet – lying dead at his feet. He threw himself down beside it. He kissed the cold red mouth. He held it in his brown arms. He kissed the closed eyes. He put the little hands round his neck.

The black sea came nearer. From the palace of the Sea King came the sound of weeping.

"The sea is coming nearer," said his soul. "If you wait, it will kill you. Come to a safe place." But the young fisherman did not listen to his soul. He said to the little mermaid, "Love is better than wisdom; love is worth more than riches; it is more beautiful than the feet of the daughters of men. I called you at sunrise and you didn't come. The moon heard me call your name, but you didn't listen to me. I was evil and I had left you and wandered away; yet my love stayed with me always and was always strong. Nothing had power against it. Now that you are dead, I will die with you."

His soul prayed him to come away, but he would not – his love was so great.

The sea came nearer and tried to cover him with its waves. When he knew that the end was near, he kissed the cold face of the mermaid, and his heart broke. His heart was broken, and his soul found a way into it, and was one with him as before.

And the sea covered the young fisherman with its waves.

In the morning the priest went down to bless the sea, for it had been troubled by the storm. When he reached the shore, he saw the young fisherman lying dead on the sand, and in his arms was the body of the little mermaid.

The Nightingale and the Rose

"She said, 'I will dance with you if you bring me a red rose'," cried the young student, "but in all my garden there is no red rose. I have studied all that the wise men have written; yet my life is spoiled because I have no red rose and don't know how or where to get one. What little things can make so great a difference to our happiness!" His eyes filled with tears.

A little nightingale heard him from her nest in the old tree. She looked out through the leaves, and wondered at him.

"Here at last I see a true lover," said the nightingale. "I have sung about true love night after night, but I never saw a true lover. Night after night I have told the story of true love to the stars and now at last I see a true lover!"

"There will be a dance at the palace tomorrow," said the student. "The prince will be there, and my loved one will be among the company. If I bring her a red rose, she will dance with me until the sun comes up into the sky. If I bring her a red rose, I shall hold her in my arms and her hand will be in mine. But there is no red rose in my garden; so I shall sit alone and she will pass me by. She won't need me, and my heart will break."

"Here indeed is the true lover," said the nightingale. "He suffers what I sing about: love is joy to me, but it is pain to him. Love is a wonderful thing. Gold and jewels can never buy it."

The student cried, "The musicians will play and my love

will dance to the music. Lords and great men, and rich men in their fine clothes will crowd round her; but she won't dance with me because I have no red rose to give her." He lay down on the grass and put his face in his hands, and wept.

"Why is he weeping?" asked the little living things in the garden. "Why is he weeping?" asked the flowers.

"He is weeping for a red rose," said the nightingale.

"For a red rose!" they cried. "How silly!" and they laughed. But the nightingale understood. She spread her brown wings and flew up into the air. She passed across the garden like a shadow.

There was a beautiful rose tree standing in the centre of a grassy place. When she saw it, she flew down to it.

"Give me a red rose," she cried, "and I will sing you my sweetest song."

"I'm sorry," said the rose tree. "My roses are white – white as the snow on the mountain. Go to my brother on the other side of the garden. Perhaps he will give you what you want."

So the nightingale flew to the other rose tree. "Give me a red rose," she cried, "and I will sing you my sweetest song."

"I'm sorry," answered the rose tree. "My roses are yellow – yellow as the golden corn in the field. But go to my brother who grows below the student's window, and perhaps he will give you what you want."

So the nightingale flew over to the rose tree which was growing below the student's window.

"Give me a red rose," she cried, "and I will sing you my sweetest song."

"My roses are red," it answered, "but the winter cold

has frozen my flowers and they have fallen, and the storm has broken my branches. I shall have no roses at all this year."

"One red rose is all I want," cried the nightingale, "only one red rose! Is there no way I can get it?"

"There is a way," answered the tree, "but I dare not tell it to you."

"Tell me the way, please," said the nightingale. "I am not afraid."

"If you want a red rose," said the tree, "you must build it out of music by moonlight and the redness must come from your heart's blood. You must sing to me with your heart pressed against a thorn. You must sing to me all night long, and the thorn must cut open your heart and your life-blood must flow into me and become mine."

"Death is a great price to pay for a red rose," cried the nightingale, "and life is very dear to us all. I love to sit in the green trees and watch the sun go down in gold and the silver moon rise up into the sky. I love to smell the flowers and wonder at their beauty. But love is better than life, and what is the heart of a bird beside the heart of a man?"

So she spread her brown wings and flew up into the air. She passed over the garden like a shadow. The young student was still lying in the grass and the tears were not yet dry in his eyes.

"Be happy," cried the nightingale. "You shall have your red rose. I'll build it out of music by moonlight, and for its redness I'll give it my own heart's blood. All that I ask of you is that you will be a true lover, for love is wiser than the wise, and stronger than the powerful."

The student looked up from the grass and listened, but he could not understand what the nightingale was saying

46

to him, for he only knew the things which are written down in books.

But the old tree understood, for he loved the little nightingale who had built her nest in his branches.

"Sing me one last song," he said. "I shall be sad and alone when you are gone."

So the nightingale sang to the old tree, and her voice was like drops of water falling from a silver jar.

When she had finished her song, the student stood up and took out a notebook.

"She has some beautiful notes in her voice, but her song does not mean anything or do any real good; it isn't really useful. She hasn't got true feeling. She thinks only of her music. She is like most artists; she thinks only of her art and herself, not about others."

He went into his room and lay down on his bed and began to think of his love. After a time he fell asleep.

When the moon shone in the sky, the nightingale flew to the rose tree. She pressed herself against the thorn. She sang all night, pressing against the thorn, and the cold moon listened. All the long night she sang, and the thorn went deeper and deeper, and her life-blood flowed away from her.

She sang first of the birth of love in the heart of a boy and a girl: and a wonderful rose came on the highest branch of the rose tree. As song followed song, it opened. At first it was white – white as the cloud that hangs over the river, silver as the wings of the morning before the sun rises up into the sky.

The rose tree cried to the nightingale to press closer against the thorn: "Press closer, little nightingale, or the day will come before the rose is finished."

So the nightingale pressed closer against the thorn, and her song became louder and louder, for she sang of the birth of love in the hearts of a man and a woman. The rose became red, but the heart of the rose remained white, for only the heart's blood of a nightingale can colour the heart of a rose.

The rose tree cried to the nightingale to press closer against the thorn. "Press closer, little nightingale," cried the rose tree, "or the day will come before the rose is finished."

So the nightingale pressed closer against the thorn. The thorn touched her heart and pain shot through her. As the pain became worse and worse, her song became wilder and wilder, for she sang of the love which is made perfect by death.

The rose became deep red. The heart of the rose was as red as a jewel. But the nightingale's voice became weaker and weaker; her little wings no longer moved, and darkness came over her eyes.

Her voice rose up in a last wonderful song. The moon heard it and waited in the sky. The red rose heard it and opened wide to the cold morning air.

"Look! Look!" cried the rose tree, "the rose is finished now." But the nightingale made no answer, for she was lying dead in the long grass with the thorn in her heart.

At midday the student opened his window and looked out.

"Ha!" he cried. "Here is a red rose! Just what I wanted! I have never seen any rose like it in all my life. I am sure it is so beautiful that it has a long name in the Latin language." So he put out his hand and took it.

Then he put on his hat and ran to the learned doctor's house with the rose in his hand. The learned doctor was

Only the heart of the rose remained white

the student's teacher, and the student loved his daughter. She was sitting at the door of the house and her little dog was lying at her feet.

"You said that you would dance with me if I brought you a red rose," cried the student. "Here is the reddest rose in all the world. You can wear it tonight next to your heart, and, as we dance together, it will tell you how I love you."

"I'm sorry," said the girl, "it won't go with the colour of my dress, and the captain has sent me some real jewels, and everyone knows that jewels cost far more than flowers."

"Well!" said the student angrily. "That's all the thanks I get!"

He threw the rose into the street and a cartwheel went over it.

"How dare you speak to me like that," said the girl. "Who are you? Only a student!" She got up from her chair and went into the house.

"What a silly thing love is!" said the student, as he walked away. "It isn't nearly as useful as reason: it doesn't prove the truth of anything. Love is always telling us of things which are not going to happen, and making us believe things which are not true. It is quite useless. In these difficult times we must learn useful things. I shall go back to my studies."

So he returned to his room, and took out a big dusty book, and began to read.

The Star Child

Two woodcutters were going home through the forest. It was winter, and very cold. There was thick snow on the ground and on the branches of the trees. The river was frozen. The snow was so deep that the woodcutters went very slowly. They were afraid that they might lose their way: it is very easy to lose your way in the snow.

At last they came to the edge of the forest and they saw far down below them the lights of the village where they lived. They were so glad that they laughed – and then they were sad. "Why do we want to live? Life is so hard for the poor. It would be better to die of cold in the forest."

Just then a very strange thing happened: a very bright and beautiful star fell out of the sky. It passed the other stars on its way and seemed to fall behind some trees quite near to them.

They ran forward. "Perhaps there will be a pot of gold where it fell!"

As the first woodcutter reached the place, he saw that there was indeed a golden thing lying on the white snow. It was a coat made of cloth-of-gold with silver stars on it. The other woodcutter came and they opened the coat so as to take the pieces of gold from it. But there was no gold there, nor silver. There was only a little child, asleep.

One of the men said, "This is a sad ending to our hopes! What use is a child to us? We are poor men and have children of our own. We mustn't give their food to another. Let's leave the child here."

The woodcutters find the child

The other man said, "That would be a very bad thing to do. We can't leave the child here to die in the cold. I'm as poor as you are, and I have many mouths to feed and not much food for them; but I'll take the child home with me, and my wife will take care of it."

So he took up the child and put the coat round it to keep out the cold and went down the hill to his village.

When they came to the village, his friend said, "You have the child; give me the coat." But the other man answered, "That coat isn't mine or yours; it's the child's coat."

Then he went to his house. His wife opened the door and saw that her man had come back safe. She put her arms round his neck and kissed him.

He said, "I have found something in the forest and have brought it to you. I know you'll take care of it."

"What is it?" she said. "There is almost nothing in this house and we need many things."

He opened the coat and showed her the sleeping child.

"Oh!" she said, "we have enough children of our own! Why have you brought this strange child to live in our house?"

"It's a star child," he said; and he told her how he found it.

"Our children haven't enough bread; must we feed and take care of some other person's child? Who takes care of us? Who gives us bread?"

"God cares for the birds and feeds them," he answered.

"And birds die of hunger in the winter," she answered, " ... and it is winter now."

A cold wind from the forest came through the open door. "Shut the door!" she said. "There's a cold wind, and I'm cold."

He said, "A cold wind always comes into a house where the heart is cold."

She did not answer, but went nearer to the fire.

After a time she turned round and looked at him, and her eyes were full of tears. He came and put the child in her arms. She kissed it and put it in the little bed where her youngest child was lying.

The next day, the woodcutter took the golden coat and put it away in a big box.

The star child was brought up with the children of the woodcutter; he sat at the table for meals with them and played with them. Every year he became more and more beautiful. All the villagers wondered at him because of his beauty.

But the star child's beauty was only on the outside: he was proud and he thought only of himself and was unkind to others. He treated the children of the woodcutter and the other children of the village badly. He said, "They are low and common people, but I am the child of a star. They are my servants."

He threw stones at the poor and those who came asking for help: "Go to some other place to ask for bread! We have none to give you!" He loved beauty; he hated and laughed at those who were weak and ugly. He loved himself. In summer he sat by the water and looked down at his own face and laughed with joy at his own beauty.

The woodcutter and his wife often spoke to him angrily: "We didn't treat you as you treat those who need help. Why are you so unkind to all who need your help?"

The star child did not listen to them but went back to the children. The children followed him because he could run fast and dance and make music. They followed wherever the star child led them and did all that he told them to do. When he put out the eyes of a little rabbit, they laughed. When he threw stones at a sick man, they laughed. They became as hard-hearted as he was.

One day a poor woman came through the village. She looked like a beggar. Her clothes were old and dirty, and there was blood on her feet, which had been cut by the stones on the road. She was very tired and sat down under a tree to rest.

The star child saw her and said, "Look at that ugly old beggar woman sitting under that beautiful green tree. Let's drive her away!"

So he came near and threw stones at her. She looked at him with fear in her eyes. The woodcutter saw what the star child was doing. He ran to him and said, "Why are you so hard of heart? What has this poor woman done to you to make you treat her like that?"

The star child was angry. "What right have you to question me? I'm not your son."

"That is true," said the woodcutter, "but I was sorry for you when I found you in the forest: I was sad because you looked so helpless; so I helped you."

When the old woman heard this she gave a loud cry and fell to the ground. The woodcutter carried her into the house and his wife took care of her. When she opened her eyes, they brought food to her, but she would not eat or drink.

She asked, "Did you say that the child was found in the forest? Was that ten years ago – just ten years ago today?"

"Yes," said the woodcutter. "I found him in the forest just ten years ago today."

"Had he a coat of gold with silver stars on it?"

"Yes," said the woodcutter. He took the coat out of the box and showed it to her.

"He is my little son that I lost in the forest. I have wandered over the whole world trying to find him." The woodcutter went out and called to the star child: "Go into the house. You will find your mother waiting there for you."

The star child ran into the house, but when he saw who was waiting for him, he laughed: "Where is my mother? I see only this dirty old beggar woman."

The woman said, "I'm your mother."

He said, "I'm not your son! You are dirty and ugly. Go away! Don't let me see your face again!"

"But you are indeed my son that I lost in the forest," she cried. She fell on her knees and held out her arms to him. "Thieves stole you from me and left you to die. But I knew you when I saw you, and I knew the coat of cloth-of-gold with silver stars. So please – please come with me. I have wandered over the whole world trying to find you. Come with me, my son, for I need your love."

But the star child did not move. He shut his heart against her. No sound was heard except the sound of a woman weeping in pain.

At last he spoke, and his voice was hard and angry. "If it is true that you are my mother, it would have been better if you had stayed away. I thought that I was the child of some star, not the child of a beggar woman as you tell me. So go! Go away and let me never see you again!"

"Won't you kiss me before I go?" she cried. "I have suffered so much to find you."

"No," said the star child. "I would rather kiss a toad or a snake!"

So the woman went away, weeping, into the forest.

The star child was glad and ran back to play with his friends. But, when they saw him coming, they said, "Go away, we won't let you play with us." And they drove him out of the garden.

"Why did they say that to me?" thought the star child. "I'll go to the water and look into it and it will tell me that I'm beautiful."

So he went to the water and looked into it. His face was like the face of a toad, and his skin was like the skin of a snake. He fell on the grass and wept, and said to himself, "This thing has come to me because I have done wrong. I have driven away my mother. I have been proud and unkind to her. I'll go and look for her through the whole world, and I won't rest until I find her."

So he ran away into the forest. He called to his mother, but there was no answer. He called for her all day. When the sun went down, he lay down to sleep on a bed of leaves. All the animals and birds ran away from him because they remembered what he had done to them.

In the morning he rose up and went on through the forest. He asked everything he met, "Have you seen my mother?" But the animals said. "You put out our eyes. You threw stones at us." And the birds said, "You cut our wings. You stole our eggs." The star child wept and asked them to forgive him and went on through the forest.

On the third day he came out of the forest and went down into open country. When he passed through villages, the children threw stones at him, and the men drove him away because they feared he might bring sickness to their animals.

He could not hear anything of the old woman who was his mother. He wandered for three years. Sometimes he seemed to see her on the road in front of him and he called to her and ran after her; but he never reached her, and people who lived near the road said, "No, we haven't seen her. There wasn't anybody on the road." They touched their heads and laughed at him.

One evening he came to the gates of a great city which stood near a river. The soldier at the gate would not let him go in. "What do you want here?" he said.

"I am looking for my mother," he answered. "Please let me pass, because she may be in this city."

"Indeed your mother will not be pleased when she sees you. You are uglier than a toad or a snake. Go away! Your mother isn't in this city."

Another soldier said "Who is your mother and why are you trying to find her?"

He answered, "My mother is a beggar – as I am too. I have treated her very badly. Please let me pass so that she may forgive me." But they would not let him go in.

As he turned away weeping, an officer came.

"Who is trying to enter this city?" he asked.

"A beggar," they answered, "and he is the child of a beggar. So we are driving him away."

"No!" said the officer, laughing. "We'll sell this thing for a slave. The price will be the price of a loaf of bread."

A strange old man was passing. He said, "I'll buy him at that price."

He paid the money and took the star child by the hand and led him into the city.

They went along many streets and came to a little door. The old man touched the door with his ring, and it opened. They went down five steps into a garden. Then the old man put a cloth over the star child's eyes and pushed him along. When the cloth was taken away, he saw that he was in a prison, lit only by a small lamp.

The old man gave him a piece of bread and said "Eat!" And he gave him a cup of water and said "Drink!" Then the old man went out. He shut and barred the door.

The old man was one of the best magicians in the world.

On the next day he came to the star child and said, "There is a small forest near the south gate of the city. In it there are three pieces of gold: one is of white gold, one is of yellow gold, and the third is of red gold. Today you must bring me the piece of white gold. If you don't bring it back, I'll beat you. Go! At sunset I'll be waiting for you at the door of the garden." Then he put a cloth over the eyes of the star child and led him through the house and the garden and up the five steps. He touched the door with his ring and it opened, and he sent him into the street.

The star child went out of the gate of the city and came to the forest.

It was a beautiful forest: the trees were beautiful, but other plants grew so thick under the trees that it was difficult to press through them, and they cut his skin. He could not find the piece of white gold anywhere. He looked for it from morning till midday and on until sunset. At sunset he turned back weeping, because he knew that he would be beaten.

As the star child came to the edge of the wood, he heard a cry. He saw a rabbit. "Set me free! Set me free!" it cried.

"I am a slave," said the star child, "but I can give you freedom." So he set the rabbit free.

The rabbit answered, "You have given me freedom. What shall I give you?"

"I'm looking for a piece of white gold. I can't find it. If I don't take it back to my master, he'll beat me."

"Come with me," said the rabbit, "and I'll lead you to it. I know where it is hidden."

So the star child went with the rabbit and found the piece of white gold, hidden in a tree.

The rabbit ran away and the star child went towards the city.

At the gate of the city there was a man whose face and skin had been eaten away by fearful illness. He had a grey cloth covering his face to hide it from people passing by so that they might not be sick at the sight of it. Two holes were cut in the cloth for his eyes. When he saw the star child coming, he rang a little bell and cried out, "Give me a piece of money or I shall die of hunger."

"I have only one piece of money," said the star child. "If I do not take it to my master, he'll beat me."

The sick man said sadly: "Please, oh please give me some money, or I shall die of hunger." The star child felt so sorry for him that he gave him the piece of white gold.

When the star child came to the magician's house, the magician opened the door and brought him in. "Have you got the piece of white gold?"

"No," said the star child. "I haven't."

So the magician beat him. Then he said, "Eat!" but he did not give him any bread; he said, "Drink", but he gave him a cup with no water in it.

On the next day the magician came to him and said, "Bring me the piece of yellow gold today. If you don't bring it, I'll beat you twice as hard and keep you as my slave."

The star child went to the forest. He tried all day to find the piece of yellow gold, but could not find it anywhere. At sunset he sat down and began to weep. As he was weeping, the little rabbit came to him.

"Why are you weeping?" said the rabbit. "What are you looking for in the forest?"

"I'm looking for a piece of yellow gold which is hidden here. If I don't find it, my master will beat me and keep me as his slave."

"Follow me," said the rabbit, and it ran through the forest till it came to a little stream. The piece of yellow gold was lying in the sand at the bottom.

"How shall I thank you?" said the star child. "This is the second time you have helped me."

"You helped me first," said the rabbit, and it ran quickly away.

The star child took the piece of yellow gold and hurried back to the city. The sick beggar saw him coming; he knelt down and cried, "Give me a piece of money, or I shall die of hunger!"

The star child said, "I have only one piece of yellow gold. If I don't take it to my master, he'll beat me and keep me as his slave." The sick man wept, and the star child felt so sorry for him that he gave him the piece of yellow gold.

When the star child came to the magician's house, the magician opened the door and took him in.

"Have you got the piece of yellow gold?"

"No," said the star child. "I haven't."

Then the magician beat him and put him back in the prison.

On the next day the magician came to him and said, "If you bring me the piece of red gold today, I'll set you free. But, if you don't bring it, I'll kill you."

The star child went to the forest. He looked for the piece of red gold all day, but he could not find it. In the evening he sat down and wept. As he was weeping, the little rabbit came to him. The rabbit said, "The piece of red gold that you are looking for is in the cave behind you. So don't weep any more but be glad."

"How shall I thank you?" said the star child. "This is the third time that you have helped me."

"You helped me the first time," said the rabbit and ran quickly away.

The star child went into the cave and in the farthest corner he found the piece of red gold. He hurried back to the city. The sick man saw him coming; he stood in the middle of the road and cried out to him, "Give me the piece of red gold or I must die."

The star child gave him the piece of red gold, saying, "Your need is greater than mine." But he was very sad because he knew what would happen to him.

As the star child passed through the gate of the city, the soldiers bowed down to him, saying, "How beautiful our lord is!" A crowd of people followed him and cried out, "There is no one so beautiful in the whole world!" The star child wept and said to himself, "They are laughing at me because I am so unhappy."

There was such a crowd that he lost his way and found at last that he was in the great square. The king's palace was in that square.

The gate of the palace opened. The high officers of the city ran out to meet him, and bowed low to him. They said, "You are our lord for whom we have been waiting. You are the son of our king."

The star child answered, "I am not a king's son. I am the child of a poor beggar woman. Why do you say that I am beautiful? I know that I am ugly – ugly as a toad or a snake."

Then an officer held up a mirror and asked: "Why does my lord say that he is not beautiful?"

The star child looked, and he saw that his face was as it had been before, but in his eyes there was something that he had not seen there before. There was love and kindness.

The high officers knelt down and said to him, "The wise men long ago told us that our king would come to us on this day. Take this crown and this sceptre and be our king."

The star child said, "It is not right that I should be your king, because I have treated my mother badly. I can't rest until I have found her and asked her to forgive me. Let me go, for I must wander again over the world. I mustn't stay here even if you give me the crown and the sceptre."

He turned away from them towards the street which led to the gate of the city. Among the crowd he saw the beggar woman who was his mother, and at her side stood the sick man who had sat by the road.

He gave a cry of joy. He ran to them and knelt down and kissed his mother's feet. "Mother," he said, "I was proud and said, 'You are not my mother.' Now I pray you to forgive me and take me as your son and give me your love." But the beggar woman did not answer.

He held out his hands and took the feet of the sick man and said, "Three times I gave you money because I was sorry for you. Ask my mother to speak to me." But the sick man did not answer.

Then he said, "Give me your forgiveness and I will go back to the forest." She put her hand on his head and said, "Stand up"; and the sick man put his hand on the star child's head and said, "Stand up."

He stood up and looked at them. They were a king and a queen.

The queen said, "This is your father. You helped him when he was the sick man."

And the king said, "This is your mother."

Then they kissed him and took him into the palace.

So the star child became king and ruled the country very well. He would not allow anyone to be unkind to birds or animals. He gave bread and clothing to the poor and was just and good to all people.

There was peace and happiness in the land.

The Selfish Giant

Every afternoon, as the children were coming back from school, they used to go and play in the giant's garden.

It was a beautiful large garden. Beautiful flowers grew in the grass. There were twelve fruit trees. In the spring the fruit trees were covered with red and white flowers, and later in the year they bore rich fruit. The birds sang in the trees so sweetly that sometimes the children stopped their games and listened to them. "How happy we are here!" they cried to each other.

One day the giant came back. He had been away for seven years. When he arrived, he saw the children playing in his garden.

"What are you doing here?" he cried in a very loud voice. The children ran away.

"My own garden is my own garden," said the giant. "I will allow no one to play in it but myself." So he built a high wall round it and put up a notice: KEEP OUT. He was a very selfish giant.

So the children had nowhere to play. They tried to play on the road, but the road was dusty and full of hard stones, and they did not like it. They wandered round the high walls when their lessons were finished and talked about the beautiful garden inside. "How happy we were there!" they said to each other.

The spring came, and there were flowers and little birds all over the country. But in the garden of the selfish giant it was still winter – the birds did not like to sing in it because there were no children, and the trees forgot to bear flowers. Snow covered up the grass, and ice covered all the trees with silver. The north wind came, and rain.

"I can't understand why the spring is so late in coming," said the selfish giant as he sat at the window of his house and looked out at his cold white garden. "I hope there will be a change in the weather."

But the spring never came, nor the summer. When there was golden fruit in every other garden, there was no fruit in the giant's garden. It was always winter there, with the north wind, and snow, and ice, and driving rain.

The giant was lying in bed one morning when he heard some beautiful music. It was a little bird singing outside his window. It was so long since he had heard the song of a bird that it seemed to him the most beautiful music in the world. Then the north wind and the rain stopped.

"I believe that spring has come at last!" said the giant. He jumped out of bed and looked out.

He saw a most wonderful sight. The children had come in through a hole in the wall and were sitting in the branches of the trees. There was a little child in every tree that he could see. The trees were so glad to have the children back that they had covered themselves with flowers, the birds were flying about and singing with joy, and flowers were looking up through the green grass.

A little boy was standing in the farthest corner of the garden. He was so small that he could not reach up to the branches of the tree, but was wandering round it and weeping. That tree was still covered with ice and snow.

"How selfish I have been!" said the giant. "Now I know why the spring would not come here. I'll put the little boy on the top of the tree. Then I'll pull down the wall and my garden shall be a children's playground for ever."

He was really sorry for what he had done. So he went down; he opened the door very quietly, and went out into the garden. But, when the children saw him, they were afraid and ran away. Only the little boy did not run: his eyes were so full of tears that he did not see the giant coming. The giant came quietly behind him. He took the little boy gently in his hand and put him up into the tree. Then the tree was suddenly covered with flowers, and the birds came and sang in it, and the little boy put his arms round the giant's neck and kissed him.

The other children saw that the giant was not bad and selfish now; so they came running back.

"It's your garden now, little children," said the giant, and he pulled down the wall.

When the people were going along the road to the town, they found the giant playing with the children in the most beautiful garden they had ever seen.

The children played all day, and in the evening they came to the giant to say goodbye to him.

"But where is your little friend?" he said. "Where is the little boy I put in the tree?" The giant loved him best because the little boy had kissed him.

"We don't know," answered the children. "He has gone away."

"You must tell him to come tomorrow; he must come tomorrow." But the children said, "We don't know where he lives. We had never seen him before." The giant felt very sad.

Every afternoon when school ended, the children came and played with the giant. But the little boy whom the giant loved was never seen again. The giant was very kind to all the children, but he did want to see his first little friend. "How much I would like to see him!" he said.

Years went by, and the giant became very old and weak. He could not play in the garden now; so he sat in a big chair and watched the children at their games and looked at his garden. "I have many beautiful flowers," he said; "but the children are the most beautiful flowers of all."

One morning, when he was dressing himself, he looked out of the window. He did not hate the winter now, because he knew that the spring was sleeping and the flowers were resting; he knew that they would come again.

Suddenly he rubbed his eyes; he looked; he looked again at the wonderful sight! In the farthest corner of the garden there was a tree quite covered with beautiful white flowers. Its branches were golden, and silver fruit hung down from them. And the little boy he loved was standing under the tree.

He ran out into the garden; he hurried across the grass to the child. Then his face became red with anger and he said, "Who has dared to wound you?" There were marks on the child's hands, and on the little feet.

"Who has dared to wound you?" cried the giant. "Tell me and I will take my sword and kill him!"

"No," said the child. "These are the wounds of love."

"Who are you?" said the giant. He was afraid, and knelt before the little child.

"You once let me play in your garden," said the child. "Today you'll come with me into my garden in heaven."

When the children came into the garden on that afternoon, they found the giant lying dead under the tree, covered with white flowers.

The child standing under the wonderful tree

Questions

Questions on each story

The Young King
1 Who brought the young king up?
2 What was the weaver making?
3 What did the slave bring up from the bottom of the sea?
4 What happened to the slave in the end?
5 What were the men doing in the dried-up river?
6 What did the young king put on his head for a crown?
7 What was the High Priest waiting for?
8 How was the young king crowned?

The Birthday of the Infanta
1 Who was the Infanta like?
2 Why were there so many things to be seen on this day?
3 What did the Infanta throw to the dwarf?
4 What did the dwarf want to tell the Infanta?
5 What did the dwarf see in the third room?
6 Where was the dwarf when the Infanta came in?
7 What order did the Infanta give in the end?

The Happy Prince
1 Where had the other swallows gone?
2 What did the little boy want?
3 What did the swallow take to the poor needlewoman?
4 Why couldn't the young man finish his story? (Because . . .)
5 What was the little girl selling?
6 What did the swallow give to the poor people?
7 What did they do with the statue of the Happy Prince?
8 What were the two best things in the city?

The Fisherman and his Soul
1 Who was the mermaid's father?
2 What did the mermaid promise to do?

3 What happened when the fisherman's boat was full of fish?
4 What did the fisherman ask the priest?
5 What did the merchants say about his soul?
6 Where was the witches' meeting place?
7 What did the young witch wear?
8 What name did the fisherman call out?
9 What did his soul ask him for?
10 Where did the fisherman go after cutting off his soul?
11 What mirror did the soul offer the fisherman?
12 What ring did he offer?
13 What did the fisherman take from the Street of the Jewellers?
14 Why couldn't his soul get into his heart while he was alive?
15 What happened to his soul in the end?

The Nightingale and the Rose
1 What did the nightingale sing about?
2 What was the student weeping for?
3 What can give redness to the rose?
4 What went into the nightingale's heart?
5 Where did the student take the rose?
6 Why didn't the girl want the rose?

The Star Child
1 What did the woodcutters find inside the coat?
2 Why did the woodcutter say, "It's a star child"? (Because . . .)
3 Why did the village children follow the star child?
4 What did the woodcutter show to the poor woman?
5 How did the woman lose her son ten years before?
6 What happened to the star child's face?
7 What did the strange old man pay for the star child?
8 How did the star child find the piece of white gold?
9 What happened to the piece of white gold?
10 Where did the star child find the piece of yellow gold?
11 What did the mirror show that was not in the star child's face before?
12 Who was the sick man the star child had helped?

The Selfish Giant
1 Why didn't the birds sing in the selfish giant's garden?
2 Why did spring come to the garden at last?
3 Why did the giant love the smallest boy best?
4 What happened to the giant in the end?

Questions on the whole book

These are harder questions. Read the Introduction, and think hard about the questions before you answer them. Some of them ask for your opinion, and there is no fixed answer.

1 The *young king* pities people of three kinds. Can you name the three kinds of people he pities?

2 The *Infanta* doesn't pity anybody. Who shows pity in the story about her?

3 a Why didn't the *Happy Prince* pity anyone when he was alive?
  b Why did he send jewels and gold leaves to people in the city?
  c What feelings do you have for the swallow?

4 a Who do you pity in the story of *The Fisherman and his Soul*?
  b What makes you pity them?

5 a Why do you feel pity for the *nightingale*?
  b Does the student have your pity? Can you explain your answer?

6 The *star child* has no pity at first, but he learns to pity. Can you give an example to show this?

7 When do you begin to pity the *selfish giant*?

8 (*The Young King*) "How are the people to know that you are a king if you are not dressed as a king?"
  a Who said those words?
  b Who were they spoken to?
  c What did he answer?
  d What, in the end, gave him the true appearance of a king?

9 (*The Birthday of the Infanta*) "Why didn't they leave me in the forest where there was no glass to show me how ugly I am?"
  a Who is the speaker?
  b How did he imagine himself before he saw the glass?
  c How did the Infanta see him?

10 (*The Happy Prince*) Was the speaker right in each of these statements? Can you explain your answer?
   a "I'm glad there is someone in the world who is happy."
   b "The needlewomen are so lazy."
   c "This has come from someone who has read my books and thinks them good."

11 (*The Nightingale and the Rose*) How did the speakers deceive themselves in these cases?
   a "Here indeed is the true lover. He suffers what I sing about."
   b "She is like most artists; she thinks only of her art and herself, not about others."
   c "Everyone knows that jewels cost far more than flowers."

12 (*The Star Child*) "Where is my mother? I see only this dirty old beggar woman."
   a Who is the speaker?
   b Who has the appearance of a beggar woman?
   c What does the star child learn about appearances in the story?

13 Which of the stories in this book did you like best? Can you give reasons for your answer?

14 Name the one person you most dislike in this book. Can you say why you dislike him or her?

New words

beggar
a very poor person who **begs**, asks for food or money

dwarf
a person of much less than the usual size for his or her age

gaol
prison

goat-herd
a person who looks after goats

melt
change from solid to liquid as an effect of heat

mermaid
an imaginary sea creature with the head, body and arms of a beautiful girl and a tail like that of a fish

mirror
a looking-glass; a shiny surface in which you can see your own face

nightingale
a small brown bird whose beautiful song is heard at night at certain seasons

sceptre
a short gold rod that a ruler carries as a sign of power

selfish
caring only for oneself, with no thought for others

statue
a figure of a person in stone or metal

swallow
a small fast-flying bird with pointed wings and a tail that ends in two points, seen in northern countries only in summer

thorn
a sharp point growing on the stem of a plant

thread
a line of twisted cotton, wool, silk, etc used in sewing

toad
a creature rather like a frog but with a rough skin

weave
make material by working threads over and under another set of threads

witch
a woman with magic powers